WRITING SKILLS

Written by **Christine Hood**

Illustrated by **Jackie Snider**

My name
is Bobby.
I live in
a

FlashKids™

This book belongs to

_____

© 2004 by Flash Kids

Colorization & Production by Creative Quotient – A Repro India Limited Enterprise

Flash Kids
A Division of Barnes & Noble
122 Fifth Avenue
New York, NY 10011

ISBN: 978-1-4114-9910-2

Please submit all inquiries to FlashKids@bn.com

Printed and bound in China

Dear Parent,

Good reading and writing skills are essential to your child's success in school. The activities in this book are designed to teach your child how to put words together to write purposefully and creatively. This book provides a variety of engaging activities meant to inspire and excite your child about writing through puzzles, letters, poetry, ads, matching, and more! To encourage your child to read and write on a daily basis, try some of the following suggestions:

- Invite your child to help you with shopping and "to-do" lists.
- Let him or her help you read and prepare a recipe.
- Involve your child in writing important dates on the family calendar, such as special events, birthdays, anniversaries, and holidays.
- Ask your child to help you write out and address thank-you cards and invitations.
- When driving together, point out street signs and addresses for your child to read and decipher.
- Create a special place in the house where you can read to your child every day!
- Let your child reward his or her work with the included stickers.
- Offer your child lots of praise and support.

Noun Story

A **noun** names a person, place, animal, or thing.

For example: friend (person)   school (place)

tiger (animal)   desk (thing)

Fill in the story below using nouns. You can make your story as silly or strange as you like. When you're finished, read your story to a friend or family member.

_____ and _____ wanted to go to
      (person)   (person)

the _____. They brought a _____ and a
    (place)   (thing)

_____. They walked five blocks. When they got
   (thing)

to the _____, they played with a _____.
      (place)   (thing)

They rode down the _____. They laid in the
          (thing)

_____. Later, they ate some _____ for a
  (thing)   (things)

snack. They saw some _____ playing nearby. It
          (animals)

made them laugh! At the end of the day they went home

in a _____. It was a good day!
   (thing)

Now make your own fill-in-the-blank story for a friend to complete!

Magic Squares

Remember, a **noun** is a person, place, animal, or thing. Use the magic squares to "magically" change one noun to another. Look at the pictures for clues.

Change **cat** to **jam** by changing one letter at a time.

c	a	t
__	a	t
__	__	__
j	a	m

Change **pin** to **mat**.

p	i	n
__	__	__
__	__	__
m	a	t

Do you notice anything special about some of the words in the magic squares? They rhyme! Write the rhyming word pairs on a separate piece of paper, and then use them in a silly rhyme.

More Magic Squares

Action words are called **verbs**. They tell what someone or something is doing, such as **laugh**, **run**, or **play**. Use the magic squares to "magically" change one verb to another. Use the pictures to help you.

Change **ran** to **hit** by changing one letter at a time.

r	a	n
__	__	__
__	__	__
h	i	t

Change **wink** to **sing**.

w	i	n	k
__	__	__	__
__	__	__	__
s	i	n	g

Now on a separate piece of paper, create your own magic squares.

Describing Words

Good writing uses interesting describing words. A describing word is called an **adjective**. Using your five senses, add describing words to each list below.

How does it:

smell?
moldy
burnt
_____
_____

feel?
rough
smooth
_____
_____

taste?
sweet
salty
_____
_____

look?
small
pretty
_____
_____

sound?
loud
clear
_____
_____

Now, choose one describing word from each list. Use each word in a sentence.

_____

_____

_____

_____

_____

Match Up!

Match each adjective to the picture it describes.

steamy

huge

prickly

cold

sugary

sour

Now, write two sentences describing one of the pictures above.
Remember to use interesting words!

_____

_____

Follow the Path

Remember, adjectives are describing words. Use a pencil to follow the path of adjectives to help Wiley Worm find the apple.

On another sheet of paper, use some of the describing words above to write a short paragraph about Wiley Worm.

How Many Ways Can You Say It?

There are many interesting words you can use to tell how something is said. For example, you can **shout**, **laugh**, or **sigh**. Find and circle interesting "saying" words in the word search below. Use the word box if you need help.

exclaim	yell	cry	whisper		
laugh	answer	ask	reply		

E	J	O	R	E	P	L	Y	W
L	X	A	E	X	C	R	R	H
A	Q	C	P	Y	E	L	L	I
U	Y	E	L	W	C	D	C	S
G	A	R	S	A	S	K	R	P
H	U	N	E	R	I	N	Y	E
X	A	Q	I	K	E	M	X	R

On another piece of paper, use at least three of these "saying" words in a short paragraph. Write about a real or imaginary chat with a friend or family member.

Say It This Way

Fill in the spaces in the story using words from the word box. Some words may fit into more than one space.

replied   asked   called   cheered   barked

Mindy _____ her mom if she could go to

the park. "Sure," Mom _____. "Will you bring

Checkers with you?"

Checkers wagged her tail and _____ loudly.

"Come on, Checkers!" Mindy _____ to her dog.

She put on Checkers's leash, and they ran to the park

together. Mindy threw a ball, and Checkers jumped in

the air to catch it. "Yeah!" Mindy _____,

clapping her hands.

What happened next?
On another sheet of paper,
finish the story. Make sure to
use interesting adjectives
and "saying" words!

Colorful Words

Adjectives can tell the color of an object. The color words below are all mixed up. "Pop" each balloon by writing the correct color word on the line below it. Use the words in the word box if you need help.

yellow   blue   red   pink
purple   brown   white   green

1. plprue

_____

2. kipn

_____

3. leub

_____

4. wbnro

_____

5. ergen

_____

6. tehwi

_____

7. lyoelw

_____

8. erd

_____

Color Rhymes

Rhymes are words that end in the same sound, like **red** and **bed**.
Complete the poem below using the color words from page 12.
If you fill in the words correctly, each two-lined verse will rhyme!

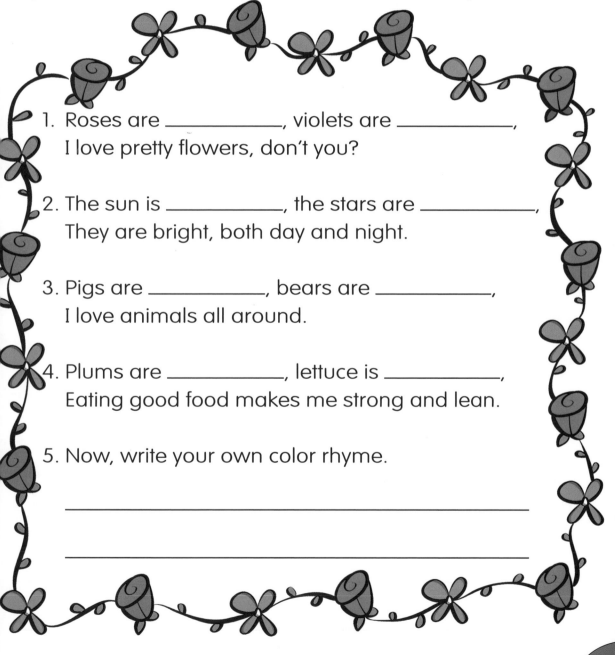

1. Roses are _____, violets are _____,
   I love pretty flowers, don't you?

2. The sun is _____, the stars are _____,
   They are bright, both day and night.

3. Pigs are _____, bears are _____,
   I love animals all around.

4. Plums are _____, lettuce is _____,
   Eating good food makes me strong and lean.

5. Now, write your own color rhyme.

   _____

   _____

Ready to Rhyme?

Follow the directions below to help Sally Squirrel find her way to the acorns.

Draw a line from Sally Squirrel to the word in row 1 that rhymes with **tree**.
Draw a line to the word in row 2 that rhymes with **blue**.
Draw a line to the word in row 3 that rhymes with **sheep**.
Draw a line to the word in row 4 that rhymes with **door**.
Draw a line to the word in row 5 that rhymes with **sing**.
Draw a line to the acorns.

1. blue   jump   walk   sea   black

2. pen   shoe   crown   king   trap

3. deep   store   cat   nut   chair

4. dress   cow   more   street   jar

5. bear   ring   lake   stop   meat

Now, write a two-line poem about Sally
using two of the rhyming words from above.

_____

_____

Ladybug, Ladybug

Complete this poem about ladybugs by writing rhyming words on the lines.

1. Ladybug, ladybug, fly around,
   Ladybug, ladybug, on the

   _____

2. Ladybug, ladybug, on a rose,
   Ladybug, ladybug, on my

   _____

3. Ladybug, ladybug, black and red,
   Ladybug, ladybug, on my

   _____

4. Ladybug, ladybug, can you stay?
   Ladybug, ladybug, don't fly

   _____

Add another verse to this poem:

5. Ladybug, ladybug,_____,

   Ladybug, ladybug,_____

Silly Rhymes

Finish each rhyme by writing a rhyming word on the line.

1. That silly goat
   Jumped off the _____!

2. My pig doesn't know what to say.
   Instead of oinking, she barks all _____!

Now, write a two-line rhyme about each picture below.

3. _____

   _____

4. _____

   _____

Crazy Compounds

A **compound word** is two smaller words put together to make one new word. Look at the picture pairs below. Write the compound word below each pair.

1.    2.

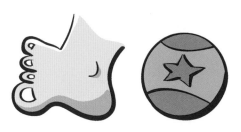

3. _____   4. _____

Now, write two sentences using at least two compound words above.

5. _____

6. _____

Onomatopoeia

A word that sounds like what it means is an **onomatopoeia**. We'll call them "sound words." For example, **buzz** and **slosh** are sound words. The letters of each sound word below are scrambled. Unscramble the letters and write them on the lines.

| pop   honk   splash   moo |

1. knoh_____

2. ppo_____

3. oom_____

4. alphss_____

Now, write sentences using at least three of the words from above.

_____

_____

_____

Capybaras Are Cool!

As you read this story, find and circle all the "sound words."

Have you ever heard of a capybara? A capybara is the largest rodent in the world, growing as big as a dog! Its name means "water pig," so you might guess that this animal is an excellent swimmer. You're right! The capybara even has webbed toes that act like paddles in the water.

This funny-looking animal lives in the rain forest. One special thing about the capybara is the sounds it makes. It purrs like a cat when it eats and barks like a dog when it's in danger. It can also click, grunt, squeak, and whistle. The capybara is a gentle animal that, if properly trained, can make a wonderful pet! It can be trained to sit up and beg, climb stairs, and walk on a leash!

Would you like to have a capybara for a pet? On a separate piece of paper, write why or why not.

How Many Words?

Below is a six-letter noun, but all of its letters are mixed up! How many little words can you make from these letters? Can you make a big word, too?

r e f n i d

1. Word with 1 letter: _____

2. Words with 2 letters: _____

3. Words with 3 letters: _____

4. Words with 4 letters: _____

5. Words with 5 letters: _____

6. Word with 6 letters (the BIG word!):

_____

Now, write about what it means to "be" the BIG word:

_____

_____

_____

_____

_____

Create a Pet

Imagine you can create your own special pet. Draw a picture of your pet, and then describe your pet on the lines below. If you need ideas, use some of the adjectives and nouns in the word box.

long	purple	fuzzy	tall	round	sharp	loud
soft	brown	curly	fluffy	nose	feet	tail	ears
legs	face	eyes	teeth	tongue	fur	scales

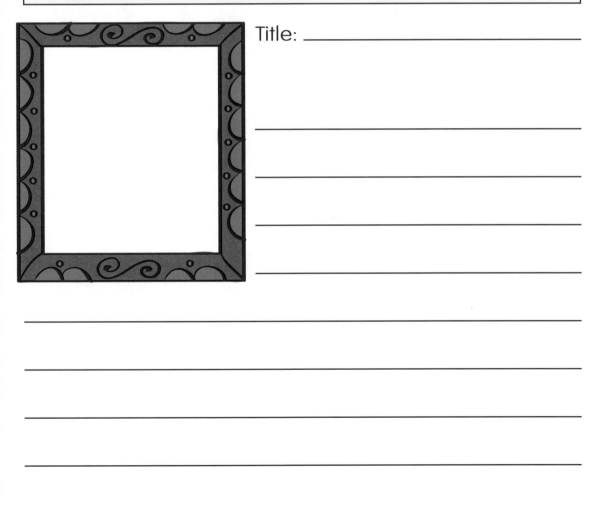

Title: _____

_____

_____

_____

_____

_____

_____

_____

Take a Guess

Guess what each set of words have in common. Write it on the line.

1.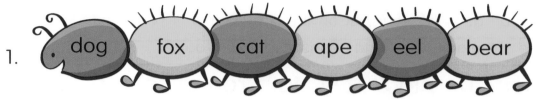

dog   fox   cat   ape   eel   bear

_____

2.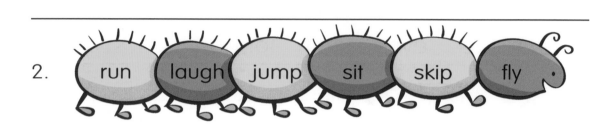

run   laugh   jump   sit   skip   fly

_____

3.

blue   big   sweet   tall   wet   smooth

_____

4.

lake   camp   park   sky   home   school

_____

Now, create your own puzzle below. Give it to a friend to solve.

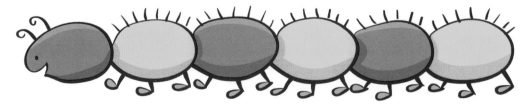

Secret Pet

Look at the **bold** words in each row. Find the letter that is in the first two words, but not in the third. Write the letter on the line. Then read the letters from top to bottom to discover your secret pet!

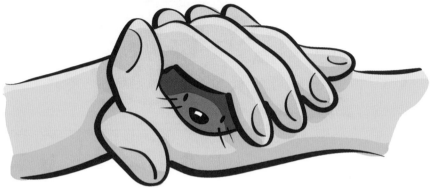

1. It's in **time** and **man**, but not in **hat**.   _____

2. It's in **joy** and **over**, but not in **vase**.   _____

3. It's in **jug** and **tube**, but not in **map**.   _____

4. It's in **is** and **sat**, but not in **hug**.   _____

5. It's in **egg** and **leg**, but not in **jar**.   _____

6. What is your secret pet?_____

7. Write three ways you can care for this pet.

_____

_____

_____

Morse Code

Morse code can be used to send secret messages! Look at the Morse code below. Use this code to solve the secret message on page 25.

A .-	**H**	**O** ---	**V** ...-
B -...	**I** ..	**P** .--.	**W** .--
C -.-.	**J** .---	**Q** --.-	**X** -..-
D -..	**K** -.-	**R** .-.	**Y** -.--
E .	**L** .-..	**S** ...	**Z** --..
F ..-.	**M** --	**T** -	
G --.	**N** -.	**U** ..-	

/ = between letters   // = between words

Break the Code

Use the Morse code on page 24 to discover the secret message. Write a letter in each box.

☐ ☐ ☐ ☐ ☐ ☐ ☐

.－－/.－./../ － /../－./－－.//

☐ ☐ ☐ ☐ ☐

../...//..－./..－/－.

Now, in the space below, write your own Morse code message for a friend or family member to solve!

Where Are You?

Circle the word in each group that does not belong.

You are here!

1	**2**	**3**	**4**
zebra	car	tennis	bush
chair	plane	monkey	tree
couch	cage	baseball	snake
bed	train	soccer	flower

5	**6**	**7**	**8**
bug	run	slam	calf
lion	walk	bang	cow
beetle	skip	zookeeper	koala
insect	ticket	crash	bull

9. Look at all your circled words. Where are you?

_____

10. Now, write three sentences about this place.

_____

_____

_____

How Can You Use It?

Find a soup ladle in your kitchen. How many ways can you think of to use this tool? For example, you can use it to scoop soup or catch a baseball. Think of other ways you can use this special tool. Use your imagination!

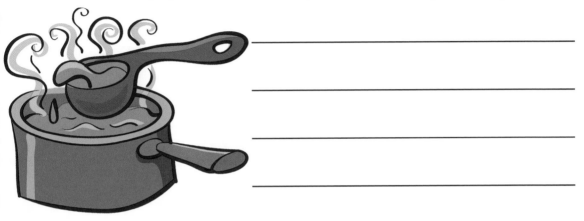

_____

_____

_____

_____

Find a bottle in your house. How many ways can you think of to use this bottle? For example, you can use it to hold a candle or you can make music by blowing over the top of it! Think of other ways you can use the bottle. Use your imagination!

_____

_____

_____

_____

Now think about another common object that has a lot of interesting uses. Write about it on a separate piece of paper.

My Favorite Holiday

Holidays are special times to share with family and friends. We often eat special foods on holidays. For example, many people eat turkey on Thanksgiving. We also do special things on certain holidays, like wear costumes at Halloween or watch fireworks on the 4th of July.

On the lines below, write about your favorite holiday. Write about the things you do, see, and eat on that special day.

Feeling Words

There are many words to describe feelings. A person can be **lonely, proud,** or **sorry**. Fill in the sentences below to tell about your feelings.

I feel proud when I work hard.

1. I feel proud when

_____

2. I feel lonely when

_____

3. I feel sorry when

_____

4. I feel shy when

_____

5. I feel doubtful when

_____

6. I feel wonderful when

_____

Think of another feeling word. Use it in a sentence on the line below.

_____

Synonym Story

Synonyms are words that have the same meaning, such as **cold** and **freezing**. **Big** and **large** are also synonyms. Replace each bold word with a synonym.

Bryan **loved** _____

playing with his pet, Ralph.

Ralph was a **small** _____, **fuzzy** _____

mouse, who sometimes **scared** _____ people. But

he was really very **gentle** _____ and could do lots

of **funny** _____ tricks.

Ralph could **leap** _____ into the air to catch a

ball. He could **spin** _____ in circles. He could find

big _____ chunks of cheese in a maze. Ralph also

liked to hide in Bryan's shirt pocket and **rest** _____

on his shoulder.

Think of some other words that describe Ralph and write them on a separate piece of paper. Also write some other words that describe your favorite pet, or a pet you'd like to have.

What Am I?

Each riddle below describes an object. Write your answer on the line.

1. I am very soft and love to cuddle. I play with balls of yarn and toy mice. What am I?

_____

2. I am tall and sturdy. Sometimes I drop things that you have to rake up. What am I?

_____

3. I can fall for hours, though I make no sound. I'm very cold, but beautiful. What am I?

_____

4. I help to wake you up in the morning. I can also tell you what time it is. What am I?

_____

On a separate piece of paper write your own "What Am I?" riddles for a friend to solve.

Who Am I?

Each riddle below describes a person.
Write your answer on the line.

1. I love to play with you. You can tell me anything, and we have lots of fun together. Who am I?

_____

2. I help you learn how to read, write, and do math problems. I am with you all year long at school. Who am I?

_____

3. I put out fires. I also help people and animals who may be trapped or in trouble. Who am I?

_____

4. I help sick people. I give them check-ups and help them stay healthy. Who am I?

_____

On a separate piece of paper write your own "Who Am I?" riddles for a friend to solve.

Where Am I?

Each riddle below describes a place. Write your answer on the line.

1. I can ride rides here. I can also play games, pet baby animals, and eat lots of fun food. Where am I?

_____

2. This is my own special place. It's where I sleep, play, and keep my toys. Where am I?

_____

3. I can find fruits, vegetables, meat, and milk here. I go to this place to buy things to eat. Where am I?

_____

4. I go here to play with friends or take a walk. There are lots of things to play on, like swings and slides. Where am I?

_____

On a separate piece of paper write your own "Where Am I?" riddles for a friend to solve.

Who? What? Where? When?

Good sentences give lots of details. When writing a sentence, try to answer these questions: **Who? What? Where?** and **When?** Use words in the word box below.

Today   game   fence   Tigers
home run   crowd   after   player

1. _____ is the big _____ against the
   (when)   (what)

   _____.
   (who)

2. The first _____ hit the ball over the _____.
              (who)   (what)

3. The _____ cheered loudly_____
        (who)   (when)

   the _____.
       (what)

Story Order

The pictures and sentences below are out of order. Number the story events **1** to **4** to put them in the correct order.

Come back, Mason!

Jon scrubbed
Mason with soap.

Jon decided to wash Mason
because he was dirty.

Oh no! Mason jumped
out of the tub!

Camping Trip

The sentences below are out of order. Number the sentences **1** to **7** to put them in the correct order.

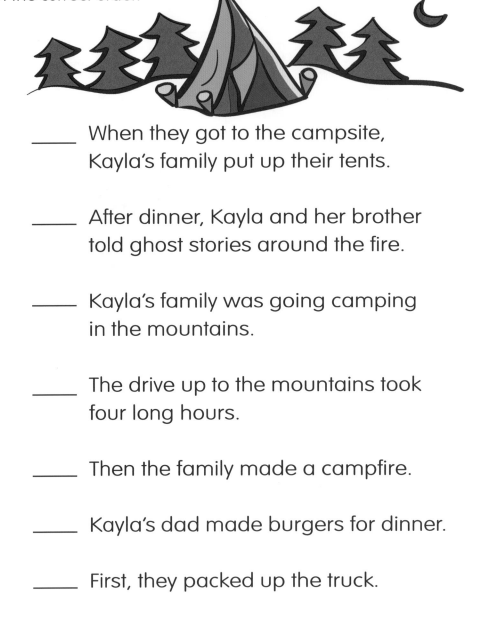

_____ When they got to the campsite, Kayla's family put up their tents.

_____ After dinner, Kayla and her brother told ghost stories around the fire.

_____ Kayla's family was going camping in the mountains.

_____ The drive up to the mountains took four long hours.

_____ Then the family made a campfire.

_____ Kayla's dad made burgers for dinner.

_____ First, they packed up the truck.

Now, on another piece of paper, write a story about the other things Kayla and her family did on their trip.

A Usual Day

What do you do each day?
Complete these sentences
to tell about what you
usually do on a school day.

I usually wake up at about _____.

Then I _____.

Next, I _____.

At school, I _____.

When I come home from school, I _____

_____.

We usually eat dinner at about _____.

I help with dinner by _____

_____.

I do my homework _____.

I always _____ before I go to bed.

On another piece of paper, write a story about what you do on a Saturday.

Fun Facts

Facts are true and can be proven. Use the secret code to find fun facts about a mystery animal. To solve the code, write the letter of the alphabet that comes **before** each letter.

a b c d e f g h i j k l m n o p q r s t u v w x y z

1. This fish can grow to be ___ ___ ___ ___ ___ feet long!
   g   p   s   u   z

2. It grows about 30,000 ___ ___ ___ ___ ___ in
   u   f   f   u   i

   its lifetime.

3. The most dangerous kind is called a

   __ __ __ __ __ __ __ __ __ __.
   h s f b u   x i j u f

4. This fish eats ___ ___ ___ ___ ___
   t f b m t

   and ___ ___ ___ ___ ___.
   t r v j e

What is the name of this mystery animal?

5. ___ ___ ___ ___ ___

Using the fun facts above, write a story about the mystery animal.

Find the Facts

Can you find the facts in this story? Read the story, and then answer the questions below.

Ladybugs are insects. They hatch from eggs. All ladybugs aren't red. They can be white, yellow, orange, pink, or black! Ladybugs eat aphids. Aphids are tiny green bugs that live on plants. Sometimes aphids can harm plants, so we call them pests. Because ladybugs eat these tiny pests, ladybugs are helpful to us. So, when you see a friendly ladybug sitting on a plant, don't shoo it away. Let it stay!

1. What are ladybugs? _____

2. What do ladybugs eat? _____

3. What are aphids? _____

Now, on another piece of paper, write your own factual story. It can be about anything you're interested in, such as racecars, ballet, or snakes. Write three or four questions about your story for a friend to answer. See if he or she can find the facts!

Fact vs. Opinion

Remember, **facts** are true and can be proven. **Opinions** are what someone feels or thinks. Read the following story. Then answer the questions below.

Fascinating Frogs

Did you know there are 2,700 different kinds of frogs and toads? Frogs and toads belong to a group of animals called amphibians. I don't like frogs because they're slimy. Frogs and toads can be big or small. They come in a variety of colors, including brown, red, yellow, green, orange, white, and blue. I would love to see a blue frog, wouldn't you?

1. Which sentences are facts? Underline them.
   How do you know these are facts?

_____

2. Which sentences are opinions? Circle them.
   How do you know these are opinions?

_____

Use an encyclopedia or the Internet to find two more interesting facts about frogs. Write them on a separate piece of paper. Also write two more opinions about frogs.

What If . . . ?

What if animals could talk?
What if you could fly?
What if you lived on the moon?

Write your answer to one of the questions above.

_____

_____

_____

_____

_____

_____

Mailbox Surprise

What would you like to find in your mailbox? Would you like to find a surprise, or a special letter? Think about all the things you'd like to discover there. List your ideas below.

_____

_____

_____

_____

Now, choose one item and write a short story about the day you discovered it in your mailbox!

_____

_____

_____

_____

_____

_____

_____

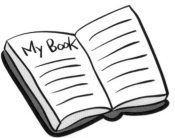

My Favorite Book

Think of a favorite book you've read. Fill out
the information below to tell about the book.

What is the title?_____

Who is the author? _____

Who are the characters? Describe them.

. _____

_____

_____

What was your favorite part of the story?

_____

_____

Write a few sentences telling someone why they should
read this book.

_____

_____

_____

Interview a Character

From the book you wrote about on page 43, choose a favorite character. Pretend you are talking to the character. How would he or she answer your questions? Write the character's answers on the lines.

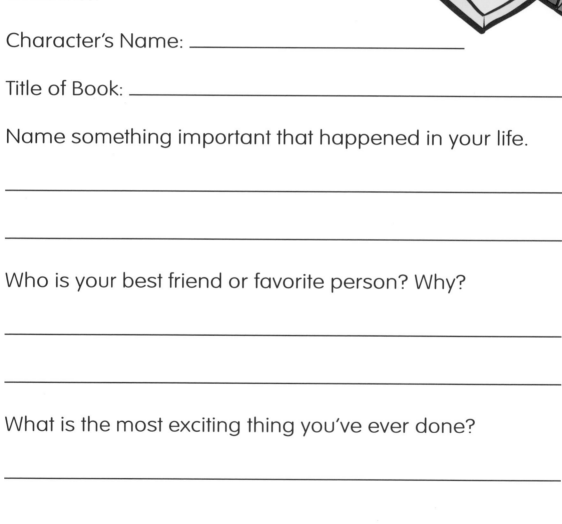

Character's Name: _____

Title of Book: _____

Name something important that happened in your life.

_____

_____

Who is your best friend or favorite person? Why?

_____

_____

What is the most exciting thing you've ever done?

_____

_____

Now, on a separate piece of paper, write a few sentences about what it was like to talk to this character.

A New Ending

Choose a favorite book or story. Then complete this page to write a new ending to the story. Don't forget to include lots of interesting details!

Title of Book: _____

How did the story end?

_____

_____

_____

What is another way the story could end? Write it below.

_____

_____

_____

Dear Diary . . .

Think of a favorite character from a book or story you've read recently. Pretend you are the character. Write a page in your diary. Tell about your thoughts and feelings during an important part of the story.

Dear Diary,

Comic Strip

In comics, characters say words in "bubbles" that come out of their mouths. These are called **speech bubbles**.

Use the comic strip below to draw a story. Be sure to include speech bubbles to show what your characters are saying! Share your comic with friends and family.

Toy Catalog

Make your own toy catalog. Cut pictures of toys from old magazines or newspapers. Glue or tape each picture into a box below. Write a sentence about each toy. Include details like size, color, shape, and why the toy is fun to play with.

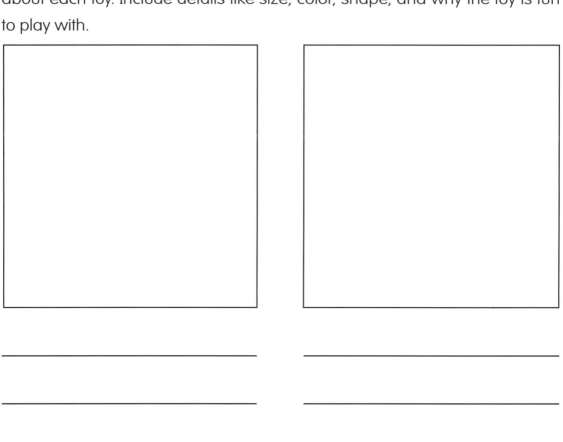

_____   _____

_____   _____

_____   _____

Wanted: Good Friend!

What kinds of things would you like to find in a friend? Someone who can help you with math? Someone who loves dogs? Someone who plays baseball? Someone who makes you laugh?

In the space below, write a want ad. Make sure to write about the exact things you want in a friend. Make your ad fun and interesting to read! Be creative!

Wanted: Good Friend

_____

_____

_____

_____

_____

You and Me

The chart below is called a Venn diagram. Use this special chart to compare yourself to a friend or family member, telling the ways you are alike and different.

In the **Me** circle, write special things about yourself. In the **You** circle, write special things about the other person. In the **Both of Us** section, write things you both have in common.

ME

BOTH OF US

YOU

Dear Friend . . .

Writing a friendly letter is easy! You can describe your day, a fun thing you've done, or a favorite trip you've taken. Write to a family member or friend on the stationery page below. When you are done, you can mail the letter!

 # Day Walk

Take a walk with a family member around your neighborhood during the day. What do you see? What do you smell, hear, and feel? Maybe you feel a light wind. Maybe you smell freshly cut grass. Maybe you hear a dog barking. Write about your senses below.

I see . . .

_____

_____

I smell . . .

_____

_____

I hear . . .

_____

_____

I feel . . .

_____

_____

 # Night Walk

This time, take a walk with your family member in the evening. What do you see? What do you smell, hear, and feel? Is it different than during the day? Maybe you see streetlights. Maybe you smell dinners being cooked. Maybe you hear televisions or cars. Write about your senses below.

I see . . .

_____

_____

I smell . . .

_____

_____

I hear . . .

_____

_____

I feel . . .

_____

_____

Thank You Very Much

When someone does something nice for you, a good way to show your thanks is by sending a special card or letter. You could send a thank-you note to your grandmother for sending you a birthday gift. You can send one to your best friend for inviting you to her party. Think of someone who has done something nice for you. Write the person a thank-you note on the lines below. When you're finished, decorate and send your letter!

Date _____

Dear _____,

Thank you for _____

_____

I liked it because _____

_____

Your kindness made me feel _____

_____

Love,

_____

Story Starter

Read the beginning of the story below. What does Jenna see? Finish this story by telling what happens next. Write your story on the lines below.

Jenna woke up and looked out her window. It looked cold and rainy outside. She guessed her softball game would be called off. Jenna decided to go downstairs to eat breakfast. But first she needed to get dressed. When she opened her closet door, she couldn't believe her eyes! It was just like her dream!

_____

_____

_____

_____

A Very Tall Tale

A **tall tale** is a story that stretches the truth. Read the beginning of the tall tale below. Then finish the story on a separate piece of paper. Remember to stretch the truth!

Burly Bear was known throughout the forest. Not only was he as tall as a five-story building, but he was also kind and brave. He protected the trees, plants, and animals of the forest. One time, Burly Bear stopped a flooding river using just his giant paw!

One morning, Burly Bear awoke to the smell of something burning. He sat straight up! Could it be a forest fire? Burly Bear saw thick black smoke rising over the tops of the trees. Being careful not to step on any animals or plants, Burly ran toward the smoke.

What happened next? Finish this tall tale on another piece of paper by telling how Burly Bear stopped the forest fire.

My Favorite Things

Use the following mini-pages to make a book about your favorite things. Complete the sentence on each page, and then draw a picture to go with it. When you're done, cut apart the pages and staple them together along the left edge.

My Favorite Things

1

My favorite color is

_____

3

My favorite place is

_____

5

My favorite book is

_____

7

My Favorite Things

My favorite animal is

_____

4

My favorite food is

_____

2

My favorite thing to do is

_____

8

My favorite friend is

_____

6

Buy, Buy, Buy!

Have you ever seen a magazine or TV ad? Ads try to tell us to buy things. Often, ads use exciting words and pictures to sell their goods.

Choose one of the items below. Write an ad to sell this item. Draw a picture to go with your ad. Use exciting words and pictures!

1. Mr. Smith's Super Sticky Pet Brush

2. Speedy Skater's Flying Skateboard

3. Acme's Glow-in-the-Dark Toothbrush

_____

_____

_____

_____

Proofreading Marks

When checking your writing, use these symbols to edit your work.

Proofreading Mark	Example
Take out a word	He ~~is~~ is nice.
Add a word	We ∧ to school. *(went)*
Add a period	Please close the door⊙
Capitalize a letter	<u>s</u>he is sad.
Make a letter lowercase	Where ⧸Do you live?
Add a comma	We have ham∧bread, and cheese.

Writing Checklist

Use this checklist to make sure you've done your best work.

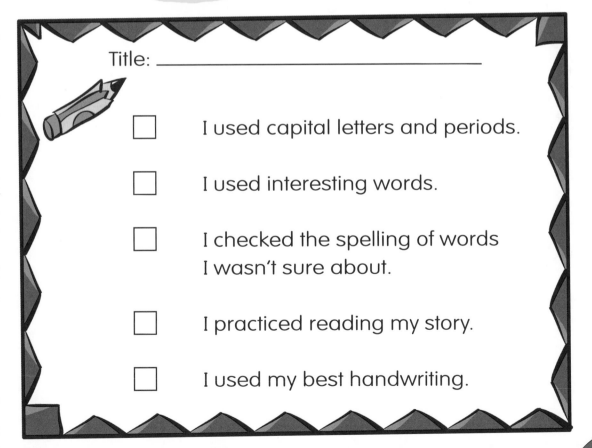

Title: _____

- ☐ I used capital letters and periods.

- ☐ I used interesting words.

- ☐ I checked the spelling of words I wasn't sure about.

- ☐ I practiced reading my story.

- ☐ I used my best handwriting.

Answer Key

Page 4
Answers will vary.

Page 5
Square 1:
cat
rat
ram
jam

Square 2:
pin
pan
man
mat

Page 6
Square 1:
ran
rat
hat
hit

Square 2:
wink
wind
wing
sing

Page 7
Answers will vary.

Page 8
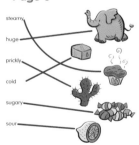

Page 9
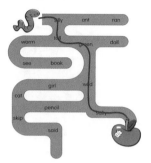

Page 10
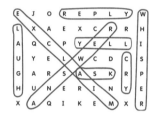

Page 11
   Mindy asked her mom if she could go to the park. "Sure," Mom replied. "Will you bring Checkers with you?"
   Checkers wagged her tail and barked loudly. "Come on, Checkers!" Mindy called to her dog. She put on Checkers's leash, and they ran to the park together. Mindy threw a ball, and Checkers jumped in the air to catch it. "Yeah!" Mindy cheered, clapping her hands.

Page 12
1. purple
2. pink
3. blue
4. brown
5. green
6. white
7. yellow
8. red

Page 13
1. Roses are red, violets are blue
2. The sun is yellow, the stars are white
3. Pigs are pink, bears are brown
4. Grapes are purple, lettuce is green
5. Answers will vary.

Page 14
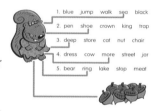

Page 15
1. ground
2. nose
3. head
4. away
5. Answers will vary.

Page 16
1. boat
2. day
3. Answers will vary.
4. Answers will vary.

Page 17
1. starfish
2. doghouse
3. fireman
4. football
5. Answers will vary.
6. Answers will vary.

Page 18
1. honk
3. pop
4. moo
5. splash

Page 19
These words should be circled: purrs, barks, click, grunt, squeak, whistle

Page 20
1. I
2. in, if
3. fin, fir, fed, den, red, rid, die, end
4. fine, find, fire, fern, rind, dine, dire, ride
5. diner, finer, fined
6. friend
7. Answers will vary.

Page 21
Answers will vary.

Page 22
1. nouns (animals)
2. verbs
3. adjectives
   (describing words)
4. nouns (places)

Page 23
1. m
2. o
3. u
4. s
5. e
6. a mouse
7. Answers will vary.

Page 25
Message: Writing is fun

Page 26
1. zebra
2. cage
3. monkey
4. snake
5. lion
6. ticket
7. zookeeper
8. koala
9. a zoo
10. Answers will vary.

Pages 27-30
Answers will vary.

Page 31
1. a cat
2. a tree
3. snow
4. a clock

Page 32
1. a friend
2. a teacher
3. a firefighter
4. a doctor

Page 33
1. a fair or carnival
2. my bedroom
3. a grocery store
4. a park

Page 34
1. Today is the big game
   against the Tigers.
2. The first player hit the
   ball over the fence.
3. The crowd cheered
   loudly after the
   home run.

Page 35
1. Jon decided to wash
   Mason because he
   was dirty.
2. Jon scrubbed
   Mason with soap.
3. Oh no! Mason
   jumped out of the tub!
4. Come back, Mason!

Page 36
1 Kayla's family was
  going camping
  in the mountains.
2 First, they packed up
  the truck.
3 The drive up to the
  mountains took
  four long hours.
4 When they got to the
  campsite, Kayla's
  family put up
  their tents.
5 Then the family
  made a campfire.
6 Kayla's dad made
  burgers for dinner.
7 After dinner, Kayla
  and her brother
  told ghost stories
  around the fire.

Page 37
Answers will vary.

Page 38
1. forty
2. teeth
3. great white
4. seals; squid
5. shark

Page 39
1. insects
2. aphids
3. tiny green bugs
   that live on plants

Page 40
Did you know there
are 2,700 different kinds
of frogs and toads? Frogs
and toads belong to a
group of animals called
amphibians. I don't like
frogs because they're
slimy. Frogs and toads
can be big or small.
They come in a variety of
colors, including brown,
red, yellow, green,
orange, white, and blue.
I would love to see a blue
frog, wouldn't you?

1. Facts can be proven.
2. Opinions are what
   someone thinks or
   feels.

Pages 41-61
Answers will vary
according to the topics
your child chooses.